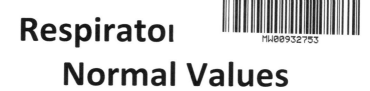

Respirator

Normal Values

Reference Guide for Students

By Johnny Lung

Disclaimer:

Medicine and respiratory therapy are continuously changing practices. The author and publisher have reviewed all information in this report with resources believed to be reliable and accurate and have made every effort to provide information that is up to date with the best practices at the time of publication. Despite our best efforts we cannot disregard the possibility of human error and continual changes in best practices the author, publisher, and any other party involved in the production of this work can warrant that the information contained herein is complete or fully accurate. The author, publisher, and all other parties involved in this work disclaim all responsibility from any errors contained within this work and from the results from the use of this information. Readers are encouraged to check all information in this publication with institutional guidelines, other sources, and up to date information. Respiratory Therapy Zone is not affiliated with the NBRC®, AARC®, or any other group at the time of this publication.

Table of Contents

Introduction

Learning all the different normal values is an important step for Respiratory Therapy Students when it comes to making informed clinical decisions. Because, if you're not familiar with what's normal, how are you supposed to know what action to take?

This is why it's so important for students to know, learn, memorize, and understand all of the required normal values. The good news is, we've listed them all out for you here to make that process easier for you.

Not to mention, questions and problems found on both the TMC Exam and Clinical Sims will include normal patient values. That means you will be required to know the normal ranges in order to select the correct answer.

Again, this is no reason to panic.

All it takes is a little bit of time and focus and you can master all of the normal values in no time. And this guide can help you learn exactly what you need to know.

So if you're ready, let's go ahead and dive right in.

Note: *In general, normal values may vary from publication to publication. With that said, we've attempted to provide the ranges that will be most helpful for the TMC Exam and Clinical Sims.*

Patient Assessment:

- **Heart Rate:** 60 – 100 beats/min
- **Respiratory Rate:** 8 – 20 breaths/min
- **Oxygen Saturation (SpO2):** > 93%
- **Blood Pressure:** 120/80 mmHg
- **Body Temperature:** 37°Celsius

Arterial Blood Gases:

- **pH:** 7.35 – 7.45
- **PaCO2:** 35 – 45 mmHg
- **PaO2:** 80 – 100 mmHg
- **HCO3⁻:** 22 – 26 mEq/L
- **BE:** -2 – +2

Normal Lab Values:

- **Hemoglobin (Hb):** 12 – 16 gm/dL
- **Hematocrit (Hct):** 40 – 50%
- **Red Blood Cells:** 4 – 6 millions/mL
- **White Blood Cells:** 5,000 – 10,000 millions/mL
- **Creatinine:** 0.7 – 1.3 mg/dL
- **Blood Urea Nitrogen (BUN):** 8 – 25 mg/dL
- **Prothrombin Time:** 11 – 15 seconds
- **Platelet Count:** 150,000 – 400,000 units
- **Troponin:** < 0.4 ng/mL
- **Brain Natriuretic Peptide (BNP):** < 100 pg/mL

Electrolytes:

- **Sodium (Na⁺):** 135 – 145 mEq/L
- **Chloride (Cl⁺):** 80 – 100 mEq/L
- **Potassium (K⁺):** 3.5 – 4.5 mEq/L

Ventilatory Values:

- **Tidal Volume (VT):** > 5 mL/kg
- **Vital Capacity (VC):** 65 – 75 mL/kg
- **Minute Ventilation (VE):** 5 – 8 L/min
- **Mean Airway Pressure (MAP):** 5 – 10 cmH2O
- **Maximum Inspiratory Pressure (MIP):** > -20 cmH2O
- **Maximum Expiratory Pressure (MEP):** > +40 cmH2O
- **Rapid Shallow Breathing Index (RSBI):** < 100
- **Deadspace-to-Tidal-Volume Ratio (VD/VT):** < 60%
- **Anatomic Deadspace:** 1 mL/pound of IBW
- **Cuff Pressure:** 25 – 35 cmH2O
- **Capnography:** 3 – 5 %
- **Intracranial Pressure (ICP):** 5 – 10 mmHg

Hemodynamic Monitoring:

- **Cardiac Output:** 4 – 8 L/min
- **Central Venous Pressure (CVP):** 2 – 6 mmHg
- **Cardiac Index:** 2 – 4 L/min/m^2
- **Stroke Volume:** 50 – 100 mL/beat
- **Pulmonary Artery Pressure (PAP):** 25/8 mmHg
- **Pulmonary Vascular Resistance (PVR):** 200 dynes/sec/cm^{-5}
- **Systemic Vascular Resistance (SVR):** 1400 dynes/sec/cm^{-5}
- **Pulmonary Capillary Wedge Pressure (PCWP):** 5 – 10 mmHg
- **Mean Arterial Pressure (MAP):** 93 mmHg
- **Urine Output:** 40 mL/hour

Oxygenation Values:

- **SpO2:** > 93%
- **PAO2:** 95 – 100% on room air
- **PaO2/FiO2 Ratio:** > 380
- **Shunt (Qs/Qt):** 3 – 5%
- **CaO2:** 17 – 20 vol%
- **CvO2:** 12 – 16 vol%
- **C(a-v)O2:** 4 – 5 vol%
- **PetCO2:** 25 – 35 mmHg
- **Oxygen Index (OI):** < 10

Pulmonary Function Testing:

- **FEV1:** > 80% of predicted
- **FEV1/FVC%:** ≥ 70%
- **Forced Vital Capacity (FVC):** > 80% of predicted
- **Slow Vital Capacity (SVC):** > 80% of predicted
- **Airway Resistance (RAW):** 0.6 – 2.4 cmH2O/L/sec
- **Diffusing Capacity for Carbon Monoxide (DLCO):** 20 – 25 mL/CO/min/mmHg
- **Peak Expiratory Flow Rate (PEFR):** 10 L/sec
- **Exhaled Carbon Monoxide:** < 7 for nonsmokers

Initial Ventilator Settings:

- **Mode:** Any mode
- **Tidal Volume:** 5 – 10 mL/kg of IBW
- **Pressure:** ≤ 35 cmH2O
- **Respiratory Rate:** 10 – 20 breaths/min
- **FiO2:** 40 – 60% or previously set level
- **PEEP:** 2 – 6 cmH2O

Infant Normal Values:

- **Heart Rate:** 110 – 160 beats/min
- **Respiratory Rate:** 30 – 60 breaths/min
- **Oxygen Saturation (SpO2):** > 90%
- **Blood Pressure:** 60/40 mmHg
- **Blood Glucose:** > 30 mg/dL
- **Gestation Age:** 40 weeks
- **APGAR Score:** 7 - 10
- **Birth Weight:** ≥ 3,000 grams
- **L/S Ratio:** ≥ 2:1
- **Silverman Anderson Score:** 0 – 1

TMC Practice Questions

As a bonus, we wanted to give you access to a few sample TMC Practice Questions so that you can get a look and feel of how the normal values will be used within some of the questions.

So if you're ready, let's get started.

1. **Hemodynamic data was collected on a 39-year-old male patient. Which of the following indicates that there is a problem with this patient?**
   A. Shunt of 7%
   B. SVR of 1400 dyn/s/cm^{-5}
   C. Cardiac Index of 3.7 L/min/m^2
   D. CVP of 5 cmH2O

To get this one correct, you simply needed to know the normal values of the hemodynamic data that is listed in the answer choices. If you can interpret that, you can easily come up with the correct answer.

- Normal shunt is 5% or less.
- Normal SVR is 1400 dyn/s/cm^{-5}
- Normal CI is 2 – 4 L/min/m^2
- Normal CVP for an adult is 2 – 6 cmH2O

By looking at the normal values, you can see that only one falls outside of the normal range and it's A.

The correct answer is: A. Shunt of 7%

2. **You are called to review the electrolyte results of an adult patient. Which of the following values is typical for serum sodium?**
   A. 127 mEq/L
   B. 132 mEq/L
   C. 141 mEq/L
   D. 158 mEq/L

You will need to know the normal values for serum electrolytes for the TMC Exam. Here they are:

- Sodium: 135 – 145 mEq/L
- Potassium – 3.5 – 4.5 mEq/L
- Chloride – 80 – 100 mEq/L

We have a shortcut inside of our **Hacking the TMC Exam** video course that makes memorizing the electrolyte normal ranges easy, so check that out if you're interested.

RespiratoryTherapyZone.com/hacking

But for this question, as long as you knew the normal values, you can easily determine that the correct answer is C.

The correct answer is: C. 141 mEq/L

3. You are called to help obtain a pulmonary capillary wedge pressure measurement using a Swan-Ganz catheter. Before the measurement is taken, the physician asks, "what is the normal range for PCWP?" Which of the following would be your response?

    A. 2 – 6 mmHg
    B. 4 – 12 mmHg
    C. 4 – 8 L/min
    D. 2 – 4 L/min/m²

For the TMC Exam, you must be familiar with the normal values for hemodynamics.

Here are a few that you should remember:

- CVP 2 – 6 mmHg
- MAP 93 mmHg
- PCWP 5 – 10 mmHg
- CO 4 – 8 L/min
- CI 2 – 4 L/min/m²

So as long as you know the hemodynamic normal values, you could easily determine that the correct answer is B.

The correct answer is: B. 4 – 12 mmHg

Well, How'd You Do?

These were just a few examples to give you an idea of some of the normal values that you need to know for the TMC Exam.

Just know that they will be used all throughout the exam which is why it's so important for you to learn this information.

The majority of questions will, in some way, contain data from the normal values that will require you to interpret it in order to select the correct answer.

So with that said, be sure to keep practicing with as many TMC Practice Questions as possible.

The practice questions that we provided for you here were actually taken straight from our **TMC Test Bank**.

It's one of our bestselling products where we break down hundreds of practice questions that cover every topic you need to know for the TMC Exam.

Each question comes with a detailed rationale that explains exactly why the answer is correct. Thousands of students have already used it to pass the TMC Exam.

Are you next?

If you thought the practice questions above were helpful, definitely consider checking it out.

To learn more, go to:

RespiratoryTherapyZone.com/tmc

Daily Practice Questions

Before you go, I just wanted to remind you about our **Practice Questions Pro** membership.

As you can most likely already tell, our practice questions are loaded with helpful tidbits of information that can help you prepare for (and) pass the TMC Exam.

Now, you can get these TMC Practice Questions sent to your inbox on a daily basis.

And the more practice questions you see, the better. This way, over time, you can master every single topic that you need to know to increase your chances of passing the exam on your first (or next) attempt.

For many students, it's very convenient to wake up each day and have a new TMC practice question in your inbox waiting for you. If this is something that sounds interesting to you, definitely consider signing up.

To learn more, go to:

RespiratoryTherapyZone.com/pro

Conclusion

So there you have it!

You now have access to all the normal values that you must know not only for Respiratory Therapy School, but for the board exams as well.

Now it's up to you to learn this information.

I definitely recommend going through the normal values several times until the information sticks. Your future self will thank you, especially once it's time to take the board exams.

No worries, I have faith in you!

Keep working and studying hard and you will be just fine. Thank you so much for reading all the way to the end.

I wish you the best of luck on your journey, and as always, breathe easy my friend.

Johnny Lung

Johnny Lung RRT

References

1. AARC Clinical Practice Guidelines, (2002-2019) Respirator Care. www.aarc.org.

2. Egan's Fundamentals of Respiratory Care. (2010) 11th Edition. Kacmarek, RM, Stoller, JK, Heur, AH. Elsevier.

3. Mosby's Respiratory Care Equipment. Cairo, JM. (2014) 9th Edition. Elsevier.

4. Pilbeam's Mechanical Ventilation. (2012) Cairo, JM. Physiological and Clinical Applications. 5th Edition. Saunders, Elsevier.

5. Ruppel's Manual of Pulmonary Function Testing. (2013) Mottram, C. 10th Edition. Elsevier.

6. Rau's Respiratory Care Pharmacology. (2012) Gardenhire, DS. 8th Edition. Elsevier.

7. Perinatal and Pediatric Respiratory Care. (2010) Walsh, BK, Czervinske, MP, DiBlasi, RM. 3rd Edition. Saunders.

8. Wilkins' Clinical Assessment in Respiratory Care (2013) Heuer, Al. 7th Edition. Saunders. Elsevier.

9. Clinical Manifestations and Assessment of Respiratory Disease. (2010) Des Jardins, T, & Burton, GG. 6th edition. Elsevier.

10. Neonatal and Pediatric Respiratory Care. (2014) Walsh, Brian K. 4th edition. RRT. Elsevier.

11. Clinical Application of Mechanical Ventilation (2013) Chang, David W. 4th edition. Cengage Learning.

Made in the USA
Las Vegas, NV
23 January 2024

84800135R00017